COLOUR Dorset

Published by Bradwell Books, 11 Orgreave Close, Sheffield S13 9NP.

Email: books@bradwellbooks.co.uk

British Library Cataloguing in Publication Data:
a catalogue record for this book is available from the British Library.

1st Edition

ISBN 9781912060764

Design and typesetting by: Andy Caffrey

Images traced by: Brian Marriott

Image Credits: All images referenced individually.

Print: Hobbs the Printers, Totton Hants.

BRADWELL
BOOKS

Looking across the rocks at the
famous Portland Bill lighthouse.

UNKNOWN PHOTOGRAPHER, USED UNDER THE CREATIVE COMMONS LICENCE

USE THESE CAMEOS TO TRY YOUR COLOUR PALLETTE
IF YOU WOULD LIKE SOME INSPIRATION FOR COLOURS, VISIT THE COLOURING BOOKS PAGE AT BRADWELLBOOKS.CO.UK

Lulworth Cove is near the village of West Lulworth, on the Jurassic Coast World Heritage Site.

BAZ RICHARDSON

USE THESE CAMEOS TO TRY YOUR COLOUR PALLETTE
IF YOU WOULD LIKE SOME INSPIRATION FOR COLOURS, VISIT THE COLOURING BOOKS PAGE AT BRADWELLBOOKS.CO.UK

The remains of the main entrance to Abbotsbury Abbey.

ANDY & SUSAN CAFFREY

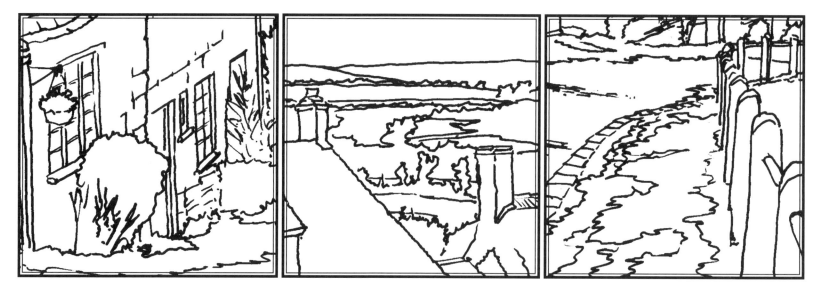

USE THESE CAMEOS TO TRY YOUR COLOUR PALLETTE
IF YOU WOULD LIKE SOME INSPIRATION FOR COLOURS, VISIT THE COLOURING BOOKS PAGE AT BRADWELLBOOKS.CO.UK

Gold Hill in Salisbury, forever famous for a bread advertisement in the 1970s.

ANDY & SUSAN CAFFREY

USE THESE CAMEOS TO TRY YOUR COLOUR PALLETTE
IF YOU WOULD LIKE SOME INSPIRATION FOR COLOURS, VISIT THE COLOURING BOOKS PAGE AT BRADWELLBOOKS.CO.UK

The picturesque harbour at Weymouth.

ANDY & SUSAN CAFFREY

USE THESE CAMEOS TO TRY YOUR COLOUR PALLETTE
IF YOU WOULD LIKE SOME INSPIRATION FOR COLOURS, VISIT THE COLOURING BOOKS PAGE AT BRADWELLBOOKS.CO.UK

A splash of colour from these beach huts in Bournemouth.

MONIKA VOLPIN, USED UNDER CREATIVE COMMONS LICENCE

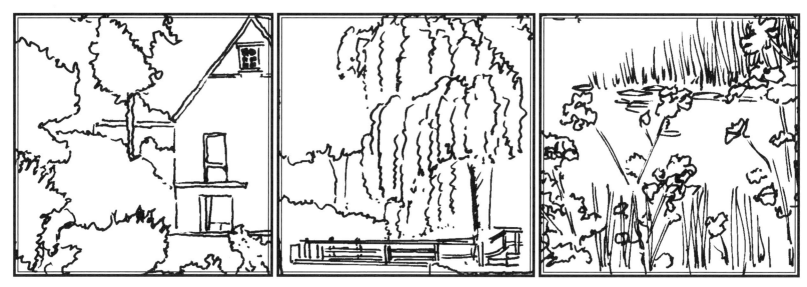

USE THESE CAMEOS TO TRY YOUR COLOUR PALLETTE
IF YOU WOULD LIKE SOME INSPIRATION FOR COLOURS, VISIT THE COLOURING BOOKS PAGE AT BRADWELLBOOKS.CO.UK

Sturminster Newton Mill an ancient flour mill built on the River Stour.

ANDY & SUSAN CAFFREY

USE THESE CAMEOS TO TRY YOUR COLOUR PALLETTE

IF YOU WOULD LIKE SOME INSPIRATION FOR COLOURS, VISIT THE COLOURING BOOKS PAGE AT BRADWELLBOOKS.CO.UK

The distinctive Umbrella Cottages.

UNKNOWN PHOTOGRAPHER, USED UNDER THE CREATIVE COMMONS LICENCE

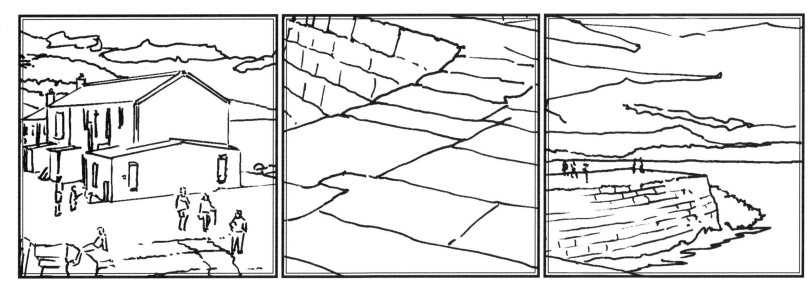

USE THESE CAMEOS TO TRY YOUR COLOUR PALLETTE

IF YOU WOULD LIKE SOME INSPIRATION FOR COLOURS, VISIT THE COLOURING BOOKS PAGE AT BRADWELLBOOKS.CO.UK

The Cob at Lyme Regis.

BAZ RICHARDSON

The majestic arch of Durdle Dore.

ANDY & SUSAN CAFFREY

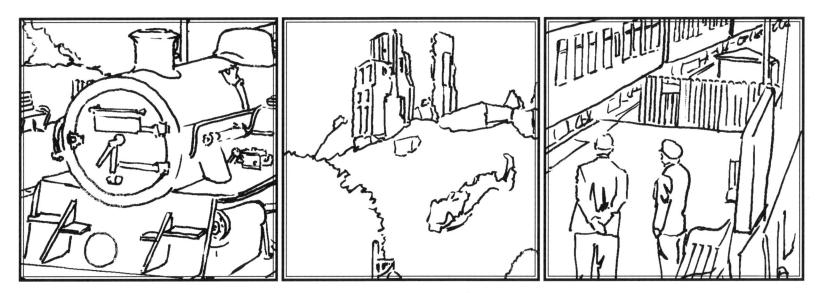

USE THESE CAMEOS TO TRY YOUR COLOUR PALLETTE

IF YOU WOULD LIKE SOME INSPIRATION FOR COLOURS, VISIT THE COLOURING BOOKS PAGE AT BRADWELLBOOKS.CO.UK

Corfe Castle station on the Swanage Railway line.

ANDREW WRIGHT

USE THESE CAMEOS TO TRY YOUR COLOUR PALLETTE

IF YOU WOULD LIKE SOME INSPIRATION FOR COLOURS, VISIT THE COLOURING BOOKS PAGE AT BRADWELLBOOKS.CO.UK

Some pretty thatched cottages in Okeford Fitzpaine.

MIKE SEARLE, USED UNDER CREATIVE COMMONS LICENCE

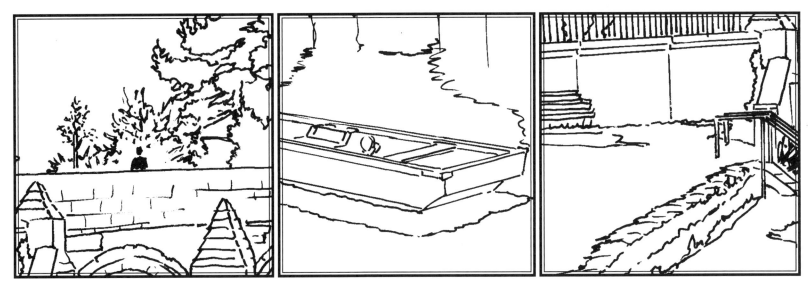

USE THESE CAMEOS TO TRY YOUR COLOUR PALLETTE
IF YOU WOULD LIKE SOME INSPIRATION FOR COLOURS, VISIT THE COLOURING BOOKS PAGE AT BRADWELLBOOKS.CO.UK

Town Bridge spans the River Avon at Christchurch.

DAVID HOWARD, USED UNDER CREATIVE COMMONS LICENCE

USE THESE CAMEOS TO TRY YOUR COLOUR PALLETTE
IF YOU WOULD LIKE SOME INSPIRATION FOR COLOURS, VISIT THE COLOURING BOOKS PAGE AT BRADWELLBOOKS.CO.UK

The old Granary on the bank of the River Frome at Wareham.

ANDY & SUSAN CAFFREY

USE THESE CAMEOS TO TRY YOUR COLOUR PALLETTE

IF YOU WOULD LIKE SOME INSPIRATION FOR COLOURS, VISIT THE COLOURING BOOKS PAGE AT BRADWELLBOOKS.CO.UK

A wonderful fossil ammonite on the Jurassic coast.

ANDY & SUSAN CAFFREY

AVAILABLE NOW

Bradwell's Images of Dorset
ISBN13: 9781910551462

Dorset Dialect
ISBN13: 9781910551011

Dorset Ghost Stories
ISBN13: 9781909914469

Dorset Wit & Humour
ISBN13: 9781909914650

Legends & Folklore Dorset
ISBN13: 9781910551493

Tales & Trivia Dorset
ISBN13: 9781910551301

Walks for All Ages Dorset
ISBN13: 9781909914339

Wessex Murder Stories: Dorset, Hampshire and Wiltshire
ISBN13: 9781912060610

www.bradwellbooks.co.uk